Barny

by Mary Gentry
Edited by Alison Hedger

A Christmas musical play with 5 new songs,
the carol, *Silent Night*, narration, dialogue and dance.
The story of how the carol, *Silent Night* came to be written.
The Bethlehem Nativity setting is created by using models of the
characters and animals made by the children.

Duration approx. 30 mins.

For children 4 to 8 years
Key Stage 1 + Lower 2

TEACHER'S BOOK
Complete with music, play and production notes.

Suitable for performance in school and church

MUSIC

1. Song – Long Ago In Austria   *All*
2. Song – Barny   *Solo + All*
3. Song – Poor Little Barny   *All*
4. Music – Tyrolean Clap Dance
5. Song – Here We Bring   *All*
6. Song – Have You Heard?   *All + Instrumental Ostinato*
7. Song – Silent Night   *a) Solo Voice or Small Group*
   b) All + Audience

A matching tape cassette of the music for rehearsals and performances is available,
Order No. GA 10907, side A with vocals included, side B with vocals omitted.

© Copyright 1994 Golden Apple Productions
A division of Chester Music Limited
8/9 Frith Street, London W1V 5TZ

Order No. GA 10894 ISBN 0-7119-4161-0

CHARACTERS

*Barny	- a mouse
Mr. Gruber	- organist
Mr. Mohr	- minister
Mrs. Mohr	
Narrator(s)	
Choir	
Villagers	
Children	- including dancers

* some solo singing and solo dancing

SCENERY

To rear of acting area a mock cardboard organ with a keyboard and cardboard tubes for organ pipes. To one side, tables or blocks for receiving the Nativity figures as they are brought up.

NATIVITY FIGURES

The children create these themselves, using papier-mâché to cover squash bottles for the bodies and polystyrene balls for the heads. The animals are made from flowerpots and cotton reels covered again in papier-mâché. The figures are finished with paints and varnish.

Mary
Joseph
Shepherds
Wise Men
Angels
Lambs
Oxen
Donkey

If preferred, a suitably sized doll dressed in swaddling clothes can be used for the baby Jesus.

COSTUMES

Barny wears a brown jump-suit and balaclava. A tail and ears are sewn onto the clothing. Dancers wear grey shorts with braces to look like "lederhosen". The choir and the minister are dressed as one would expect in church. The children and Mrs. Mohr wear brightly coloured clothing.

"I wrote BARNY for my class of 14 children aged 6-8 years, in a small First school. The children had to be villagers, choir, children and dancers, as well as the main characters! However, the play is well suited for larger numbers if available. I hope you enjoy BARNY as much as we did. We were invited to sing the song HERE WE BRING in our local church. The children carried their Nativity figures and placed them in situ for the Christmas season. This was a very worthwhile experience for them, having lovingly made models which were then shared by the local community."

Mary Gentry

BARNY

Narrator   Our story begins a long time ago in a village in Austria. The harvest celebrations have been over for some time and all the fruit and flowers have been taken away. The church is empty. Or so it would appear!

Enter choir who sing centre front.

1. SONG   LONG AGO IN AUSTRIA

All

1. Long ago in Austria
   A little mouse lived alone.
   He lived in the church
   In a village set on a hill.

2. All his friends and family
   Visited him each year
   To enjoy the harvest at the
   Little church on a hill.

3. When the church was dark and still,
   His family slipped away
   To their own cosy nests
   In the village set on a hill.

Choir exit. Enter Barny.

Barny   I do wish some of my less hungry close family would stay here with me. I like it here – especially as Christmas will be the next big celebration. By the way, I'd better introduce myself.

Clears his throat importantly.

2. SONG   BARNY

Solo

1. I'm a regular a lad, a bit of a cad,
   And Barny is my name.
   I live in comfort at the church
   And cadging is my game. But when they
   Clean the church
   The ladies search,
   And if they glimpse me, scream.
   They all shout " A mouse, get out, get out, get out, get out,
   And don't come back again."

All   They all shout "A mouse, get out, get out, get out, get out,
            And don't come back again."

Solo	2. I'm a popular chap, my friends all clap When I sing a song or two. My elegance when I dance Won me a waltzing blue. But when they Clean the church The ladies search, And if they glimpse me, scream. They all shout "A mouse! Get out, get out, get out, get out, And don't come back again."
All	They all shout "A mouse! Get out, get out, get out, get out, And don't come back again."

Barny dances during next verse.

All	3. He's a regular lad, a bit of a cad, And Barny is his name. He lives in comfort at the church And cadging is his game. But when they Clean the church The ladies search, And if they glimpse him scream. They all shout "A mouse! Get out, get out, get out, get out, And don't come back again." They all shout "A mouse! Get out, get out, get out, get out, And don't come back again."

Solo CODA	Good evening friends.
Barny	Hmmmm! All those cousins of mine. At least sixty of them! They've eaten me out of house and home. Still, I expect something will turn up. It usually does.

Barny exits.

Narrator	As winter drew on, Barny ran out of food. He had to hunt for every crumb. He grew thinner and thinner and weaker and weaker. He explored every corner of the church trying to find anything to eat. Anything to keep his hunger at bay.

3. SONG   POOR LITTLE BARNY

3R
Mice

All
1. Poor little Barny, he's so hungry,
   Lonely and afraid.
   No more nuts or grain in his store.

2. Poor little Barny, sad and empty.
   What is he to do ?
   No more nuts or grain in his store.

3. Hungry, Barny's hungry.
   No more nuts or grain in his store.
   Hungry, Barny's hungry.
   He needs more food.

Narrator   Barny curled up in a corner and fell asleep. In the village
everyone was getting ready for Christmas. The children danced in
celebration.

4.   TYROLEAN CLAP DANCE

* Waist coats

Children enter and dance and clap in time with the music, then exit.

3W

Narrator   The week before Christmas there was a procession to the church
to make a Nativity scene. Barny hid near the organ, feeling faint
with hunger.

Barny   I hope they can't hear my tummy rumbling!

5. SONG   HERE WE BRING

They Come

*During the song children/villagers enter carrying their Nativity figures and place them to one side,
building up a setting of the crib scene.*

they come
1. Here we bring Joseph and Mary,
   Place them carefully in the stable.
   Here we bring Joseph and Mary,
   Place them gently 'round the crib.

   he is
2. Here we bring baby Jesus,
   Place Him carefully in the stable.
   Here we bring baby Jesus,
   Place Him gently in the crib.

5

3. Here we bring shepherds and wise men,
   Place them carefully in the stable.
   Here we bring shepherds and wise men,
   Place them gently 'round the crib.

[handwritten: Liz's class + ½ the]
[handwritten: Shepherds + lambs]
[handwritten: Sing song]

4. Here we bring oxen and donkey,
   Place them carefully in the stable.
   Here we bring oxen and donkey,
   Place them gently 'round the crib.

[handwritten: Cath's class + ½ the]
[handwritten: animals]
[handwritten: Sing song]

5. Here we bring little lambkins,
   Place them carefully in the stable.
   Here we bring little lambkins,
   Place them gently 'round the crib.

6. Here we bring beautiful angels,
   Place them carefully in the stable.
   Here we bring beautiful angels,
   Place them gently 'round the crib.

[handwritten: Yr I   Angels]
[handwritten: Sing song   Star]

[handwritten: Away in a Manger]

Children/villagers exit. Barny comes out of hiding.

Barny   Oh my poor tummy! I'll simply have to find something to chew.

He examines the organ. Takes a bite and nibbles it.

Leather, ugh! Pretty revolting, but it will have to do.

Narrator   Barny chewed for a while and then settled down near the crib, finding a snug place to hide. Two days later Mr. Gruber the organist came to the church to practise the Christmas carols.

Enter Mr. Gruber rubbing his hands together, and sits at the organ.

Mr. Gruber   Right! I think we'll have a nice long carol to begin with. Good King Wenceslas.

He plays the organ but he only gets a few odd noises.

Oh no!

He examines the back of the organ, and shouts in dismay.

Holes! Mice! I must see the minister, at once!

Mr. Mohr the minister enters.

Mr Gruber	Mr. Mohr, Mr. Mohr - disaster has struck! Some perishing little mouse has eaten parts of the organ and now it won't play. There's nothing for it - you'll have to cancel Christmas.

Mr. Mohr	That's a bit drastic, my friend. Now calm down. Does the organ make any sound at all?

Mr Gruber	Only this.

He plays again and the same odd noises are heard.

I'd get more than these few squeaks out of the mouse if I could lay my hands on it.

Barny	Ooooooo, errr !
(still well hidden)

Mr. Mohr	Come to my house Mr. Gruber and we'll talk about this together.

Exit Mr Gruber and Mr Mohr.

Narrator	Poor Barny felt awful. He felt terrible. He felt so very, very sorry.

Barny
(sings to last section of melody to Song POOR LITTLE BARNY)

Sorry, I'm so sorry.
I didn't mean to cause any harm.
Sorry, I'm so sorry.
I've spoilt Christmas for everyone.

Barny sadly returns to hiding place.

Narrator	Meanwhile Mr and Mrs Mohr and Mr Gruber are having a meeting.

Mr and Mrs Mohr and Mr Gruber enter and sit in a semi-circle on chairs.

Mrs. Mohr	Can't we have singing without the organ?

Mr. Gruber	Don't be silly.

Mr. Mohr	Well then, what about your guitar Mr Gruber?
Mr. Gruber	We can't possibly sing Good King Wenceslas to a guitar!
Mrs. Mohr	Why don't you write a new carol then, using what notes we do have left after you've repaired what you can!
Mr. Gruber	Just like that! Write a new carol?
Mrs. Mohr	I'm sure Mr. Mohr will help you with the words, won't you dear?
Mr. Mohr	Certainly.
Mr. Gruber	Oh well. I can but try!

Exit Mrs. Mohr

Narrator	Together Mr. Gruber and Mr. Mohr worked away writing a carol. It took them nearly all night.

Exit Mr Gruber and Mr. Mohr

The next day was Christmas Eve. *Here they come song*

6. SONG   HAVE YOU HEARD ?

(with optional instrumental ostinato)

Enter villagers gossiping and agitated. #4 Everybody + cleaning ladies

All	Have you heard, have you heard That there'll be no music at the service on Christmas Eve? It can't be true! But they say that a mouse has nibbled through the organ, Made holes in the bellows. Mister Gruber's sad and angry. Mister Gruber's sad and angry.

(sing song through twice)

(Solo villager or group,
speaking over music)

CODA	That mouse will die. We'll make nice mouse pie!
Narrator	That evening all the villagers made their way to church for the service.

All enter

The minister began the service with an announcement.

| **Mr. Mohr** | My friends, a mouse has nibbled the organ and even after Mr. Gruber has repaired it, I am afraid that it still won't play some of the notes properly. |

Villagers mutter disappointedly.

| **Barny**
(from hiding place) | I feel awful. |

| **Mr. Mohr** | However, Mr. Gruber has written some music for a new carol, using the notes that do play properly. We have called it Silent Night. One (*or a group*) of the children has learnt it, and will now sing it to you. |

7 a)   SILENT NIGHT

Solo or group 1. Silent night, holy night.
All is calm, all is bright
Round the gentle Mother and Child.   *choir*
Holy Infant so tender and mild,
Sleep in heavenly peace,
Sleep in heavenly peace.

| **Mr. Mohr** | I think you will agree with me that the little mouse in question has done us a good turn. Without him, we wouldn't have our beautiful new carol! |

| **Narrator** | When Barny heard this he gave out a huge sigh of contentment. He crept out of hiding and snuggled up in front of the crib. One child crept up and gave Barny something to eat.

Ever since that night, people all over the world have enjoyed singing the carol Silent Night. We now ask you to join with us, and sing this carol together. |

7b)   SILENT NIGHT

Franz Gruber 1787–1863
Joseph Mohr 1792–1848

1. Silent night, holy night.
All is calm, all is bright
Round the gentle Mother and Child.
Holy Infant so tender and mild,
Sleep in heavenly peace,
Sleep in heavenly peace.

2. Silent night, holy night.
Guiding star lend your light.
See the eastern wise men bring
Gifts and homage to the King.
Christ the Saviour is here,
Christ the Saviour is here.

3. Silent night, holy night.
Wondrous star, light so bright.
With the angels let us sing
Alleluias to our King.
Christ the Saviour is here,
Christ the Saviour is here.

After a word of thanks to the cast etc. repeat verse 3 of the song BARNY *for exits and taking of bows.*

THE END

1
LONG AGO IN AUSTRIA

Cue: Or so it would appear!

1. Long a - go in Aust - ri - a a lit - tle mouse lived a - lone. He lived in the church in a vil - lage set on a hill.

2. All his friends and fam - i - ly vis - i - ted him each year to en-

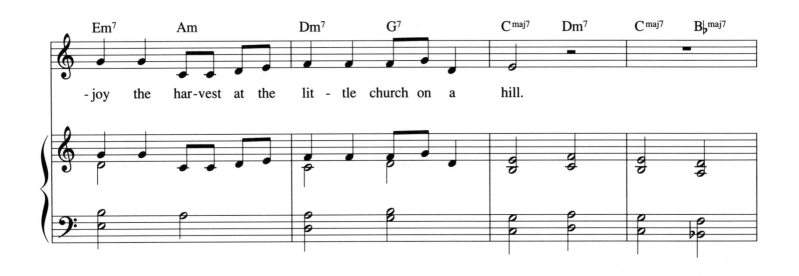

-joy the har-vest at the lit - tle church on a hill.

3. When the church was dark and still, his fam-i - ly slipped a - way to their

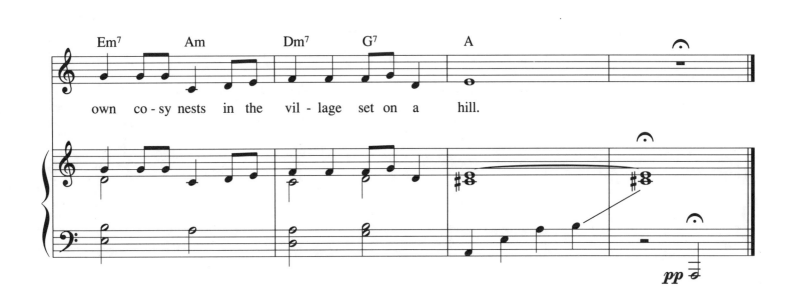

own co - sy nests in the vil - lage set on a hill.

2
BARNY

Cue: By the way, I'd better introduce myself.

After a word of thanks to the cast etc., sing and play verse 3 for exits and taking of bows.

Lyrics under the staves:

Solo 1. I'm a reg - u - lar lad, a bit of a cad, ___ and Barn - y is my
pop - u - lar chap, my friends ___ all clap when I sing a song or
reg - u - lar lad, a bit of a cad ___ and Barn - y is his

name. ___ I live in com - fort at the church and cadg - ing is my
two. ___ My el - e - gance ___ when I dance won me a waltz - ing
name. ___ He lives in com - fort at the church and cadg - ing is his

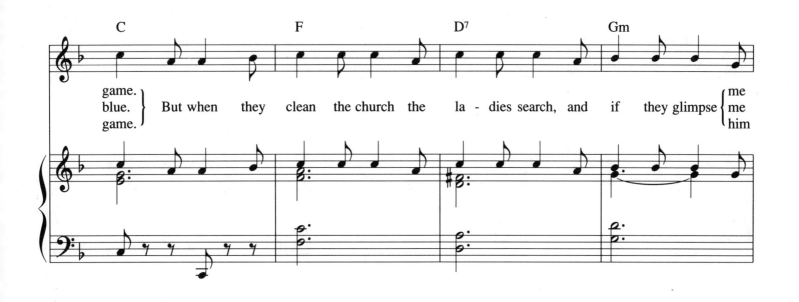

game.
blue. } But when they clean the church the la - dies search, and if they glimpse { me
game.   { me
                                                                                   { him

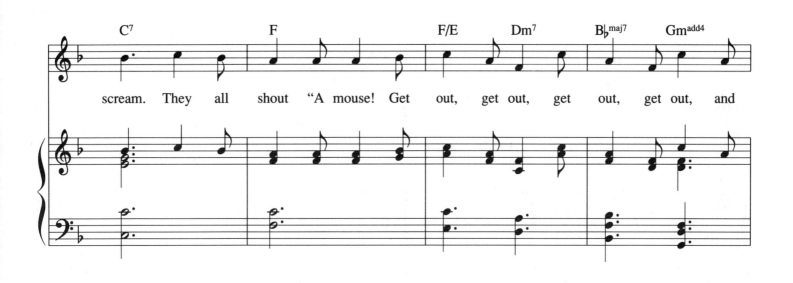

scream. They all shout "A mouse! Get out, get out, get out, get out, and

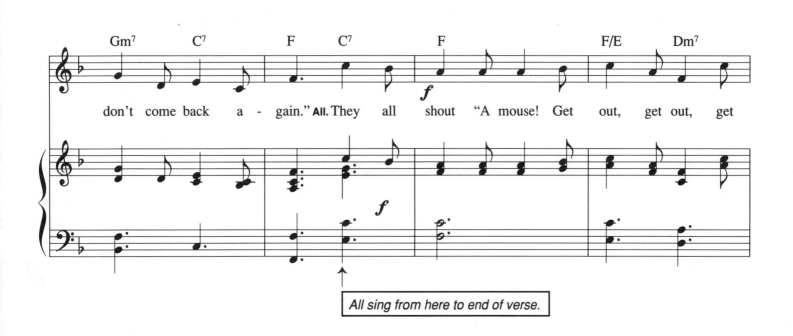

don't come back a - gain." **All.** They all shout "A mouse! Get out, get out, get

All sing from here to end of verse.

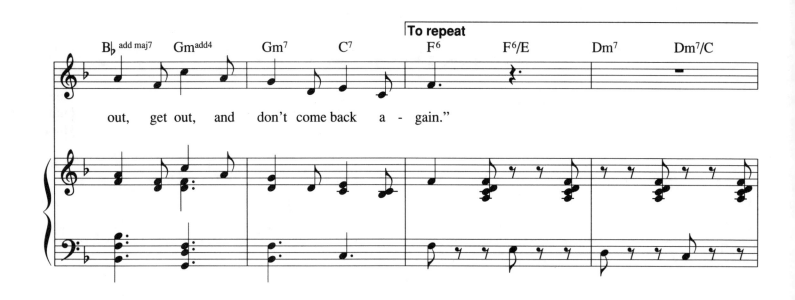

out, get out, and don't come back a - gain."

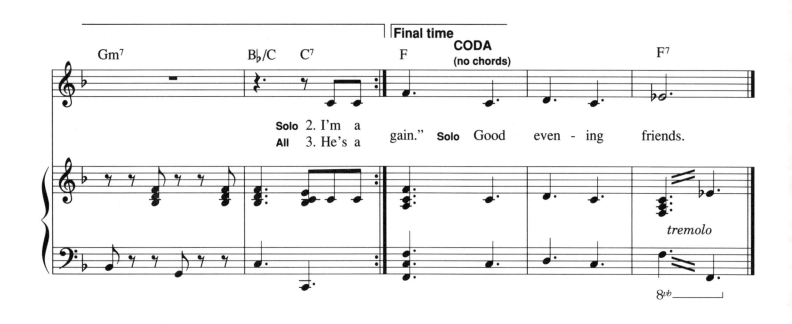

Solo 2. I'm a
All 3. He's a

gain." Solo Good even - ing friends.

POOR LITTLE BARNY

Cue: Anything to keep his hunger at bay.

Sing twice

Sadly ♩ = 100

1. Poor lit - tle Barn - y, he's so hun - gry,
2. Poor lit - tle Barn - y, sad and emp - ty.

lone - ly___ and a - fraid. No more nuts or grain in his store.
What is he to___ do? No more nuts or grain in his store.

3. Hun - gry, Barn-y's hun - gry.

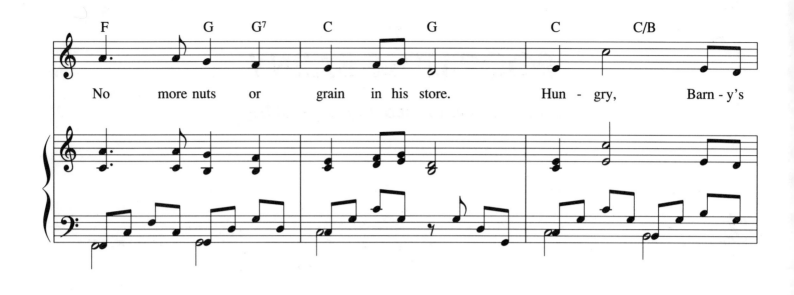

No more nuts or grain in his store. Hun - gry, Barn - y's

hun - gry. He needs more food.

Unaccompanied solo for Barny. See script, page 7.

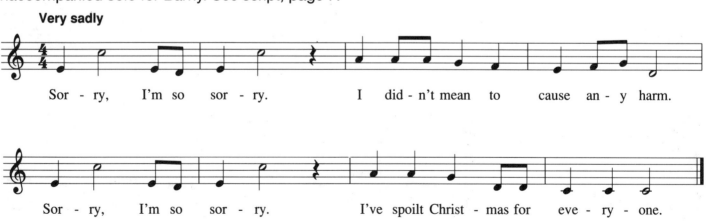

Very sadly

Sor - ry, I'm so sor - ry. I did - n't mean to cause an - y harm.

Sor - ry, I'm so sor - ry. I've spoilt Christ - mas for eve - ry - one.

4
TYROLEAN CLAP DANCE

Cue: The children danced in celebration

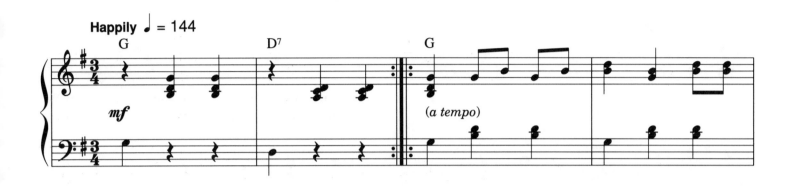

5
HERE WE BRING

Cue: I hope they can't hear my tummy rumbling!

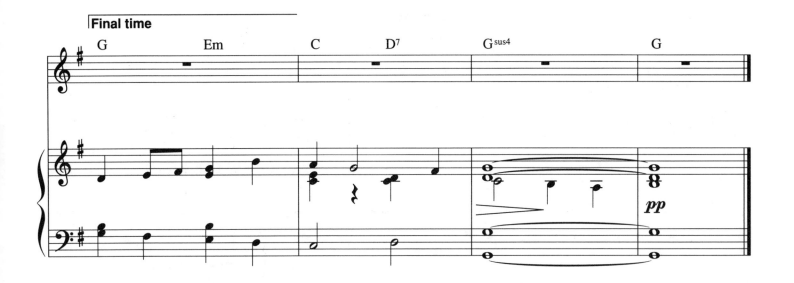

3.   Here we bring shepherds and wise men,
Place them carefully in the stable.
Here we bring shepherds and wise men,
Place them gently 'round the crib.

4.   Oxen and donkey

5.   Little lambkins

6.   Beautiful angels

6
HAVE YOU HEARD?

with optional instrumental ostinato

Cue: The next day was Christmas Eve.

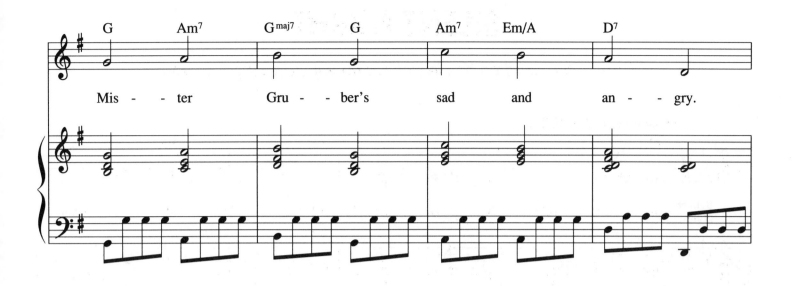

Mis - ter Gru - ber's sad and an - gry.

1st time

2nd time

Mis - ter Gru - ber's sad and an - gry. Have you an - gry.

CODA (speak over music)

Solo or group That mouse will die. We'll make a nice mouse pie!

(NO OSTINATO)

7a
SILENT NIGHT

Cue: ...the children has learnt it, and will now sing it to you.

With simplicity ♩ = 100

Solo or group

Si - lent night, ho - ly night. All is calm, all is bright

round the gen - tle Moth - er and Child. Ho - ly In - fant so ten - der and mild,

sleep in heav - en - ly peace.___ Sleep___ in heav - en - ly peace.

Introduction

7b
SILENT NIGHT

Franz Gruber 1787–1863
Joseph Mohr 1792–1848

Cue: …join with us, and sing this carol together.

1. Silent night, holy night.
   All is calm, all is bright
   Round the gentle Mother and Child.
   Holy Infant so tender and mild,
   Sleep in heavenly peace,
   Sleep in heavenly peace.

2. Silent night, holy night.
   Guiding star lend your light.
   See the eastern wise men bring
   Gifts and homage to the King.
   Christ the Saviour is here,
   Christ the Saviour is here.

3. Silent night, holy night.
   Wondrous star, light so bright.
   With the angels let us sing
   Alleluias to our King.
   Christ the Saviour is here,
   Christ the Saviour is here.

Printed and bound in Great Britain by
Caligraving Limited Thetford Norfolk